Involving the Public –

One of Many Priorities

A survey of public involvement in London's

primary care groups

Will Anderson

Dominique Florin

Published by

King's Fund Publishing
11–13 Cavendish Square
London W1M 0AN

© King's Fund 2000

First published 2000

ISBN 1 85717 422 4

A CIP catalogue record for this book is available from the British Library

Available from:

King's Fund Bookshop
11–13 Cavendish Square
London
W1M 0AN

Tel: 020 7307 2591
Fax: 020 7307 2801

Printed and bound in Great Britain

Contents

Acknowledgements

Summary 1

1. Introduction 2

2. Methods and sample 3

3. One of many priorities.. 4
    3.1 Absolute and relative priorities 4
    3.2 The obstacles to developing public involvement 7
    3.3 The priority areas for public involvement 7

4. Making public involvement happen... 8
    4.1 Whose responsibility? 8
    4.2 Lay members and their roles 9
    4.3 Resources and training.. 11
    4.4 The role of the community health council................................. 12
    4.5 Strategies 12

5. Public involvement in practice... 13
    5.1 Aims 13
    5.2 Objectives... 14
    5.3 Target groups 16

6. Discussion: capacity and commitment... 17
    6.1 Integrating public involvement into PCGs' work....................... 17
    6.2 Building relationships with patients, carers and the public......... 18
    6.3 Finding the appropriate level of public involvement.................. 18
    6.4 Defining success in public involvement for PCGs...................... 19

References 20

Acknowledgements

We would like to thank all our respondents for their time and interest; Mary Burkett, Veronica Cotterill, Nicholas Reeves, Peter Westland and Liz Wise for their crucial feedback during the pilot stage; Steve Gillam, Ros Levenson, Maria Duggan, Brian Fisher and Christine Farrell for their support and advice; and Shanaz Islam and Robyn Preston for their patience with the data.

Will Anderson & Dominique Florin
April 2000

Summary

Public involvement is a high priority for the majority of chief executives and lay members in primary care groups (PCGs) in London. However, in a time of rapid organisational change, there are many high priorities. The principal obstacles to public involvement have been lack of time and resources and the demands of other more pressing concerns.

PCGs have rarely left responsibility for public involvement solely with their lay members. Despite the obstacles, corporate approaches to public involvement are widespread, reflected in shared responsibilities, delegated working groups and the development of PCG public involvement strategies.

Lay members typically bring considerable knowledge and experience of local communities to PCG boards. However, the extent to which they can personally sustain a 'community voice' is disputed. Despite this ambiguity in their role, many lay members have played a key part in advocating for, enabling and undertaking public involvement initiatives.

Financial investment in public involvement has been meagre to date, but most PCGs have undertaken some form of public involvement training and sought professional advice from those with greater experience of public involvement.

In pursuing public involvement, PCGs' principal aim has been to inform and influence their decision-making and service development. However, there have been many other aims served by public involvement initiatives, including informing, educating and empowering the individuals and communities who make up the many possible 'publics' with which PCGs engage. The creation of open and accountable processes and the development of good relationships with community stakeholders are also seen by some as important outcomes in themselves.

Most of the public involvement methods and objectives identified by PCGs concern communication and consultation rather than more participative or community-driven forms of involvement. The latter will require greater resources and a longer-term shift in organisational and professional values.

1. Introduction

This report provides a snapshot of user and public involvement within primary care groups (PCGs) in London, based on the views of their chief executives and lay members. It is the first output of a two year study conducted by the King's Fund Primary Care Programme which will describe and evaluate the approaches to public involvement adopted by PCGs in the capital.

The project is funded by the Health in Partnership initiative, a Department of Health programme promoting user and public involvement in the NHS. This initiative builds on a decade of public involvement policy in the NHS, spanning *Local Voices,*[1] the *Patients Charter,*[2] the *Patient Partnership Strategy*[3] and *The new NHS – modern, dependable.*[4] Current government policy promotes open decision-making in NHS institutions, as well as a consumerist agenda of shaping services to the needs and wants of users.[4]

The creation of PCGs included two formal mechanisms for public involvement: the appointment of a lay member to every PCG board and the requirement for open board meetings. However, the broader agenda requires that PCGs take account of local views;[5] allow the public to participate in decision-making;[5] communicate with stakeholders[6] and foster opportunities for public involvement.[6]

Promoting public involvement is one of the King's Fund's core aims. Although this report's title reflects a realism about current constraints within PCGs, we hope that the content will be useful to those who are pursuing meaningful public involvement in primary care.

2. Methods and sample

The study employed two self-complete postal questionnaires, one designed for chief executives and one for lay members. They were piloted before being disseminated to the chief executives and lay members in London's 66 primary care groups in October 1999. All PCGs were phoned to check receipt of the questionnaires and two follow-up letters were sent to the chief executives.

Questionnaires were returned from 58 out of a possible 65 chief executives (89 per cent response rate) and 47 out of a possible 65 lay members (72 per cent response rate). Sample sizes for specific results are sometimes smaller due to incomplete questionnaires.

One or both questionnaires were returned from 65 PCGs (99 per cent). However, the subsamples of chief executives and lay members reflect two slightly different subsets of these 65 PCGs. There is an overlap of 40 PCGs from which both the chief executive and lay member returned a questionnaire. The two subsamples are kept separate in the results: either one sample is used or the two samples are used comparatively; there are no results which combine data from the two subsamples.

3. One of many priorities

3.1 Absolute and relative priorities

In order to assess the place of public involvement among PCG priorities, respondents were asked to state the priority they gave to thirteen issues relevant to PCG development.

For each issue, respondents gave a value in the range 1 (low priority) to 5 (high priority). On the single issue of 'developing public involvement', three quarters of the chief executives (76 per cent) gave a value of 4 or 5. Furthermore, nearly all (91 per cent) of the lay members gave a value of 4 or 5. On this measure alone, commitment to public involvement appears to be widespread.

Many respondents gave a high priority to all 13 issues. Hence the *relative* priority of public involvement gives a more meaningful indication of where it actually sits within personal and organisational commitments. For each respondent, we identified whether the value they gave to public involvement was higher than their average (median) value across all 13 issues, lower than their average, or equal to their average.

Figure 1 illustrates chief executives' personal priorities. It is immediately obvious where their energies are focused: on infrastructure, finance, developing primary care and clinical governance. Developing public involvement is the ninth priority out of 13, with only 16 per cent of chief executives identifying public involvement as a higher than average priority. Thus, in relative terms, public involvement is rarely a high priority for PCG chief executives.

Using an identical list, respondents were also asked how they perceived the priorities of their boards. Figure 2 illustrates chief executives' perceptions of board priorities. The category order used in Figure 1 is repeated here, thereby showing up any differences between chief executives' own priorities and their perceptions of board priorities. Developing public involvement was identified by only 16 per cent of chief executives as a higher than average priority for their boards. The only major difference between their own priorities and those of their boards (as they perceived them) was prescribing policy: one in two chief executives (50 per cent) felt this was a higher than average board priority, compared to one in five (19 per cent) for whom it was personally a higher than average priority. They also felt that infrastructure and finance were less of a concern to their boards.

Lay members' priorities were very different from those of the chief executives – and from those of their own boards. Figure 3 illustrates their own priorities. Although primary care development and clinical governance are as important to lay members as they are to chief executives, developing public involvement was most often identified as a higher than average priority (by 61 per cent of lay members). In relative terms, public involvement remains a high priority for lay members.

Figure 4 illustrates lay members' perceptions of the priorities of their boards, using the same category order as Figure 3. Unlike chief executives, whose personal priorities appeared to be roughly congruent with their boards', lay members perceived their boards' priorities to be quite different from their own. Developing public involvement was perceived to be a higher than average board priority by only 9 per cent of lay members.

Figure 1: Personal priorities of chief executives

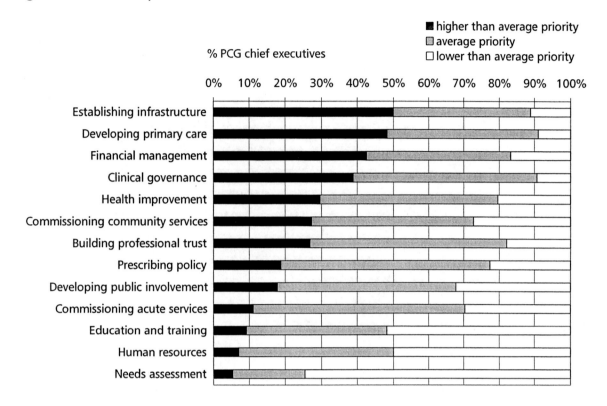

Figure 2: Chief executives' perceptions of board priorities

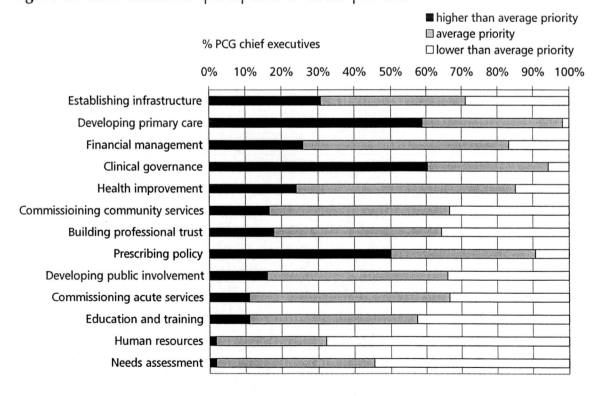

Figure 3: Lay members' personal priorities

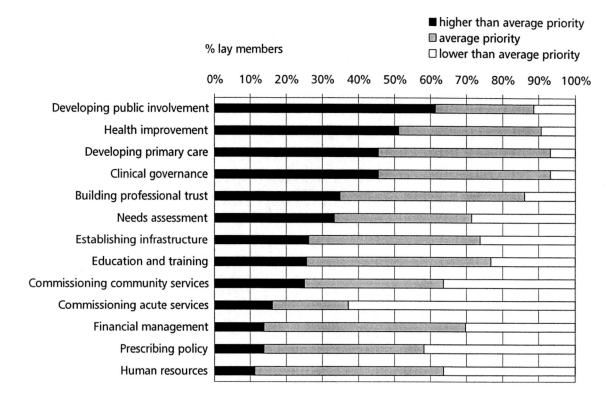

Figure 4: Lay members' perceptions of board priorities

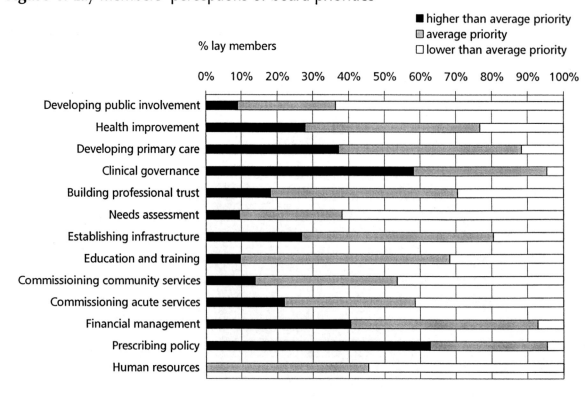

3.2   The obstacles to developing public involvement

The evidence above suggests that there is considerable commitment – in principle – to pursuing public involvement among chief executives and lay members, but that the many demands upon PCGs limit the opportunities to exploit this commitment. This view is supported by respondents' descriptions of the obstacles to public involvement in their PCGs. These overwhelmingly concern organisational capacity rather than fundamental doubts about public involvement itself.

Chief executives and lay members identified a range of obstacles to developing public involvement. Overall, they were dominated by one broad concern: the limited time and resources of PCGs and the size of the development agenda. Forty five out of 57 chief executives (79 per cent) and 29 out of 39 lay members (74 per cent) identified this as a problem.

A wide range of other obstacles were identified. However, none were mentioned by more than ten chief executives or ten lay members. These included:

- the attitudes of board members or primary care professionals, including reticence, apathy, paternalism and defensiveness
- the limitations of available skills, experience and understanding of public involvement
- lack of public interest and the difficulties of reaching the local population
- lack of clarity about what PCGs' public involvement role should be
- too many organisations pursuing public involvement and a lack of collaboration.

These secondary obstacles all concern the specific challenges of taking forward public involvement, rather than the basic need for organisational capacity. It may be that the overwhelming lack of time and resources currently masks these obstacles, which may become more prominent as public involvement initiatives develop.

3.3   The priority areas for public involvement

Chief executives were asked if any public involvement had taken place as part of their implementation of five key areas of responsibility: clinical governance, primary care development, health improvement, commissioning and needs assessment.

For each area, only a minority reported any public involvement work to date. The highest report of public involvement was as part of health improvement, where 43 per cent of chief executives reported some activity. Public involvement activity was reported in primary care development by 38 per cent of chief executives, in commissioning by 31 per cent and in clinical governance by 24 per cent.

4. Making public involvement happen

The last section identified lack of time and resources as major obstacles to developing public involvement. This section explores the ways in which PCGs are managing the public involvement agenda, despite these obstacles.

A key question is: *who* should make public involvement happen? The study explored this question in two ways: by identifying who had specific responsibility for public involvement on PCG boards; and by investigating the role of the lay member.

4.1   Whose responsibility?

Chief executives indicated whether there were any board members who had specific responsibility for public involvement. Table 1 illustrates the results. Out of 58 chief executives, two reported that no-one on the board had specific responsibility for public involvement and two reported that everyone did. These responses may, of course, reflect very similar corporate approaches to tackling the issue. Other respondents also made clear in their comments that public involvement was a matter for the whole board, whatever the form of delegation to individual members.

Table 1: Delegation of responsibility for public involvement to PCG board members

Board member	No. PCGs (n=58)	% PCGs
Lay member	51	88
Chief executive	40	69
Chair	17	29
GP members	16	27
Nurse members	8	14
Health authority non-executive member	7	12
CHC co-opted members or observers	5	9
Social services member	4	7

Although these results indicate that lay members are almost universally charged with a responsibility for public involvement, they usually have the support of others. In all but eight PCGs, specific responsibility for public involvement was shared, at least in principle. In the eight PCGs where only one person had specific responsibility, six delegated this to the lay member, one to the chief executive and one to the nurse member.

Two thirds (63 per cent) of the PCGs had subgroups or working groups addressing public involvement and a further 21 per cent were planning one. Of the six lay members who had sole responsibility on the board for public involvement, only two had no support (or planned support) from such a subgroup.

Thus PCGs' formal governance arrangements demonstrate a corporate interest in public involvement which goes well beyond leaving the matter with the lay member. Public involvement may not be at the top of PCG priorities, but nor is it relegated to a token add-on. This does not mean, of course, that lay members feel adequately supported in their role, or that the formal mechanisms adopted for pursuing public involvement are, in practice, appropriate to the task.

4.2   Lay members and their roles

The lay members brought considerable experience of working for public, voluntary and community organisations to their PCG boards. None described professional backgrounds completely outside these sectors. Table 2 describes the range of their experience. Almost two thirds (63 per cent) of the lay members identified previous experience as board members, trustees, councillors or governors.

Table 2: Professional and voluntary experience of lay members

Sector	No. lay members (n=43)	% lay members
Voluntary/community	31	72
Education	14	33
NHS	11	26
Local authority (not education)	8	19
CHC	6	14
Academic	5	12
Church	2	5

Fifty chief executives and 46 lay members described what they considered the role (or roles) of the lay member to be. Figure 5 illustrates the analysis of their responses.

The 'unique perspective' which many respondents felt that lay members brought to PCG boards was variously described as 'lay', 'non-medical', 'user' or 'independent'; and also as 'providing a check to the board's decision-making', 'questioning professional assumptions' or 'being the conscience of the board'. Although this personal perspective is integral to the lay member's role, there was no consensus as to whether it included a special relationship with the local community, such as representing patients or the community, being a voice for local people or providing a local community perspective. In the following quotes, the ambition of this role is clear:

To represent the local community in decisions affecting local people and to advise the board about what people expect from primary care.

To provide a perspective of the public and the voluntary sector in all aspects of the PCG's main functions.

To advise the board on how the wider community is engaging, or otherwise, in PCG business.

Table 2 demonstrates that lay members are experienced in social and community issues – a resource which PCGs would be foolish to ignore. Yet, as several lay members made clear, this does not necessarily mean that they were in a position to represent the community or voice community views. Resolving this tension appropriately was a key concern for many lay members.

A role in advocating or enabling public involvement was identified by half (49 per cent) of the lay members and half (50 per cent) of the chief executives. This included championing the development of public involvement, leading specific initiatives and ensuring that the views of local people were included in the PCG's work and decision-making. A majority of the lay members (56 per cent) also identified a particular role for themselves in outreach and communication for the PCG: liasing with community organisations, ensuring two-way communication between board and the community and finding out the views of local people. These two roles – advocating/leading and undertaking public involvement – were closely linked. Overall, three quarters (73 per cent) of lay members and two thirds (64 per cent) of chief executives included promoting or doing public involvement in the lay member's role. What this actually meant in practice varied considerably, as the following quotes show:

To advise the board on mechanisms to develop public and patient involvement.

To constantly remind the board of the duty and benefits of involving the public.

To liase with community health council and voluntary groups and bear these in mind when contributing to the board.

Figure 5: The role of the lay member

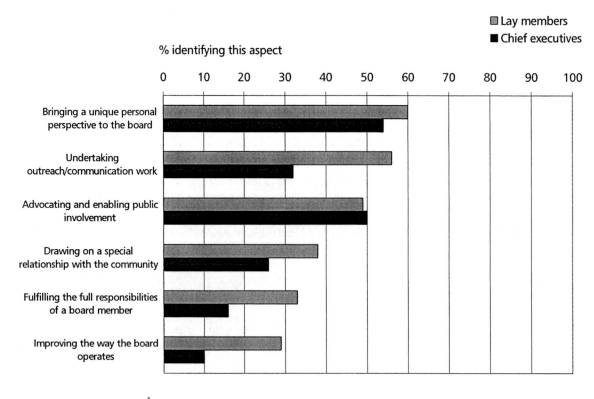

To relay the PCG's priorities and plans to lay audiences and to develop an understanding of the voluntary sector and user/patient groups.

A minority of lay members (33 per cent) and chief executives (16 per cent) described the lay member's role in terms of the general responsibilities of board membership: being a full member of the board and contributing to all aspects of the board's work. This general aspect of board membership may have seemed self-evident to other respondents – those who stressed it were usually making the point that the lay member's role should not be marginalised to specific aspects of the board's business. Some lay members (29 per cent), and a few chief executives (10 per cent), also identified specific ways in which the lay member could improve the workings of the board as a whole. This encompassed a number of possibilities: promoting a user-oriented perspective among all board members, encouraging open and accountable process and improving the quality of the board's communication to the public, particularly the transparency of the language used.

Overall, these results demonstrate the range of potential contributions that lay members can make to the work and decision-making of PCGs. As lay members, they remain an integral component of any PCG's lay involvement process. However, there is a variety of related roles that lay members have taken in relation to the broader public involvement process – as advocates, proxy managers, field workers and advisers – as well as trying to fulfil their responsibilities as ordinary board members.

There is also tension between these roles – above all, between acting as an ordinary board member, contributing to all the board's responsibilities, while also being expected to sustain a special role in relation to the local community.

4.3   Resources and training

If PCGs are putting corporate effort into public involvement and drawing on the resources of the lay member to do so, what resources are being put in to the process? Half (47 per cent) of chief executives reported that specific financial resources had been dedicated to public involvement, ranging from £1000 to £24,000. Some respondents made clear that significant funding was not yet appropriate, given the stage of development of public involvement initiatives.

Chief executives also reported whether training, resources and advice in public involvement had been received by the lay member, some of the board members or the whole board. Figure 6 illustrates the results. The 'other' sources of advice included community health councils (five mentions), management consultants (two mentions) and the King's Fund (two mentions).

All the PCGs had done something, over a third (37 per cent) had provided all three key interventions (training, resources and some form of advice) and only 9 per cent had provided only one of these interventions.

In practice, advice from the health authority may simply mean the contribution of the health authority non-executive member, and published resources could encompass everything from health service circulars (HSCs) to detailed handbooks. Nonetheless, this is further evidence that public involvement is enjoying some degree of corporate investment, even if the financial resources commited to date have not been great.

4.4   The role of the community health council

There is no consensus about what the relationship between community health councils (CHCs) and PCGs ought to be. There was a marked difference between those lay members who reported that the CHC had been important to them and the majority who described the CHC role as having been minor or limited to attending PCG board meetings.

Where CHCs had played a more active role, this included providing regular advice and support to the lay member; organising special public involvement initiatives; and bringing together local stakeholders.

These results support evidence from the Greater London Association of Community Health Councils indicating that, both on and off PCG boards, CHC officers and members are adopting very diverse roles.[7]

4.5   Strategies

Twenty five chief executives (43 per cent) reported that the PCG had a strategy addressing public involvement and 28 (48 per cent) were planning one. Five (9 per cent) had neither a strategy nor plans to produce one.

Figure 6: Resources and training on public involvement

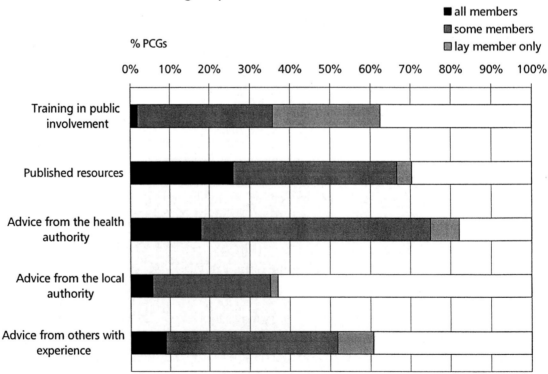

5. Public involvement in practice

National guidance on public involvement makes it clear that PCGs must work with their local communities and promote openness, accountability and public confidence in the NHS. But there is little detail about what, in practice, PCGs should actually do to promote public involvement. Consequently, PCGs are working out for themselves the form and content of local public involvement initiatives.

5.1 Aims

Chief executives and lay members were asked to state what they felt the aims of public involvement in the PCG should be. The analysis of the responses of 55 chief executives and 45 lay members is illustrated in Figure 7.

The dominant aim, cited by 89 per cent of chief executives and 71 per cent of lay members, was for public involvement to inform and influence organisational decision-making and planning. Similar interests are reflected in the aims of improving standards of service delivery and assessing and responding to needs. Most respondents did not specify the nature of the decisions in which they wanted involvement. However, some chief executives (20 per cent) and lay members (13 per cent) specifically wanted to see public input to priority-setting.

These results beg the question of how much influence respondents actually wanted the public to have in PCG decision-making. The language used by respondents in the following quotes illustrates the range of possibilities:

Figure 7: Aims of public involvement

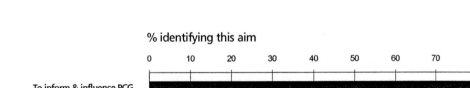

To shape and influence the work of the PCG in every aspect of our role.

To establish partnership in developing future health priorities.

To get views on the PCG work programme.

To comment on policies and proposals.

Many of the identified aims concerned immediate outcomes for the public themselves, rather than (or in addition to) outcomes for the organisation and its professional consituents. In particular, 31 per cent of chief executives and 40 per cent of lay members identified public involvement as a route to informing and educating local people. However, the emphasis was on informing and making people aware of the PCG and local health services. A few respondents described educational aims about improving personal health and using services and treatments appropriately. Others saw this not as an educational process but as a process of enabling people to gain control over their health and health care (identified separately in Figure 7).

Just as there were different views about the level of involvement of the public in the work of the PCG, so there were different views about the level of engagement of the PCG with the public. The following quotes illustrate these different levels of engagement:

To communicate the role of the PCG to the community.

To educate the public in their rights and in services available to them and how to access them.

To support the development of models of consumer empowerment.

Public involvement was not always perceived as a means to an end. Better engagement and communication with the local community and encouraging accountable and open process were both seen as valid outcomes in themselves.

All these aims are inextricably linked and most respondents identified more than one. PCGs need to recognise their interdependence and consider how to maximise the related outcomes of public involvement in the initiatives they develop.

5.2   Objectives

Aims come before objectives in rational planning, but not always in practice. Respondents' objectives for public involvement provide a more pragmatic view of their work and interests. Fifty two chief executives and 34 lay members identified up to three 18-month objectives for public involvement (see Figure 8).

Objectives were described in diverse ways. Chief executives were more likely to specify the areas of work in which they wanted involvement than the actual methods they would use, whereas lay members were more focused on methods. Objectives were also described in terms of target groups, settings (e.g. practice-based initiatives) and processes (e.g. strategy development, joint-working).

Over half of the chief executives (56 per cent) and 29 per cent of the lay members identified areas of work in which they wanted public involvement. Beyond 'service planning', these were dominated by the three PCG core functions of primary care development, health improvement and (to a lesser extent) commissioning. Only two chief executives and two lay members stated objectives specifically related to clinical governance. Other areas in which involvement was planned included primary care trust consultation, Healthy Living Centre bids and PCG priority-setting.

Specific methods of public involvement in the PCG, described by half (48 per cent) of the chief executives and three quarters (74 per cent) of lay members, included:

● regular community or stakeholder meetings
● special public events such as one-off consultation meetings and health fairs
● patient surveys (run through specific practices but designed to inform the whole PCG)
● local workshops and focus groups
● community-based needs assessments
● consultation through existing networks.

The communication methods described were newsletters, leaflets and posters, with only one mention of a website. The development of practice-based involvement mainly concerned setting up or supporting patient participation groups. Other approaches included providing training and materials to encourage patient-professional partnership and establishing patient representatives in local practices to feed in to broader PCG consultation mechanisms.

Figure 8: Eighteen-month objectives

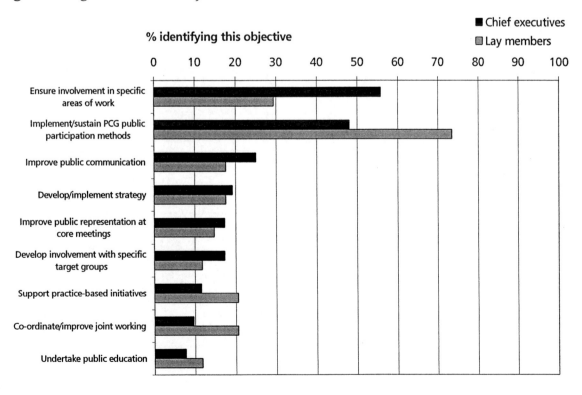

Other objectives reflected internal organisational views of what success in public involvement would look like: producing and/or implementing a strategy, getting lay representation on subgroups and improving collaboration and joint working.

5.3 Target groups

Some respondents identified target groups among their objectives, but greater detail was provided by the chief executives in response to a question which specifically asked whether any targeted public involvement work had taken place within PCGs. Of the 56 who answered the question, a quarter (27 per cent) said that some targeted work had been undertaken, half (52 per cent) said they had plans to do some, with the remainder (21 per cent) claiming neither to have done any work nor to have any plans.

Thirty six chief executives stated which groups they had worked with or planned to work with. Table 3 describes their responses. The patient groups identified included people affected by coronary heart disease, diabetes, mental health problems, asthma and HIV.

Table 3: Target groups identified by chief executives

Target group	No. CEs identifying this group	% CEs identifying any target group (n=36)	% all CEs (n=56)
Patient groups/service users	18	50	32
Minority ethnic communities	11	31	20
Asylum seekers and refugees	10	28	18
Older people	6	17	11
Children and young people	6	17	11
Socially disadvantaged areas/individuals	4	11	7
Families	4	11	7
Homeless people	3	8	5
Carers	3	8	5
Drug users	3	8	5
People with disabilities	1	3	2
Unregistered patients	1	3	2

6. Discussion: capacity and commitment

The title of this report highlights the reality of corporate life during primary care groups' first year of existence. Within an overwhelming operational and development agenda, public involvement has rarely been a high priority for PCG boards. Limited time and resources have inhibited the integration of public involvement into the work and decision-making of PCGs.

If this central conclusion is discouraging, it nonetheless provides a realistic vantage point from which to assess the public involvement activity which is actually taking place within PCGs in London. Most chief executives and lay members claim that public involvement is a high personal priority, even if it does get crowded out by other concerns. Almost all PCG boards share responsibility for public involvement and a majority have designated subgroups or working groups addressing the issue; most have public involvement strategies or are developing them; and many PCG board members have received relevant training, resources or professional advice. PCG's plans for public involvement suggest that they have responded creatively to the agenda set by the Department of Health. Overall, PCGs' corporate commitments to public involvement have been considerable.

These headline conclusions contrast realism about the place of public involvement among PCG priorities with optimism about the emergence of an organisational culture supportive of public involvement. In practice, this culture may still feel very fragile in many PCGs, particularly if commitment to public involvement is not shared by board members other than the lay member and the chief executive. Other recent research in primary care has described a tension between individuals' commitments to public involvement and the longer-term fragility of their achievements.[8]

6.1 Integrating public involvement into PCGs' work

The desire to ensure that public involvement is integral to how NHS organisations work has been voiced within health care for some time[9] and is now prominent in national guidance.[10,11] This study suggests that the value of a corporate approach to public involvement is increasingly acknowledged within PCGs in London, at least by the lay member and chief executive – who are most likely to have responsibility for leading on the issue. Data from the current national evaluation of PCGs indicate that a majority of chairs also see public involvement as being a corporate responsibility.[12]

Corporate commitment may reflect progress towards integration of public involvement into primary care, but full integration is likely to be a long term project, requiring a profound shift in professional values and practice. The evidence from this study suggests that professional values are not widely felt to be an obstacle to public involvement. However, the process of accepting the changing role of patients and the public will require that professionals and organisations rethink all of the ways that they relate to users and the public.

PCG board members who see integration of public involvement as their principal task may be setting themselves up to fail. The lack of time and capacity reported by so many respondents may, for some, reflect a sense of the enormity of the public involvement agenda. A radical long term vision needs to be balanced by realistic short and medium term expectations, defined by the resources and opportunities available. Although the widespread development of public involvement strategies is encouraging, it is crucial that such strategies achieve this balance.

6.2   Building relationships with patients, carers and the public

PCGs must consider how they engage with all their constituent 'publics'. The strategic role of PCGs has encouraged many to consider their responsibilities to all members of their local communities, not just their immediate users. Although patient groups were common targets for involvement, there was also considerable interest in involving those marginalised by economics, culture or the services themselves. The key role of carers was, however, rarely acknowledged. Engaging across the diversity of local communities and patient and carer interests requires considerable time and resources, the very things which PCGs lack.

Lay members are the most controversial 'community resource' within PCGs, because of the different views about their role. PCGs which expect their lay members to have a special relationship with the community and/or act as a conduit to patients' views may not be acting in the best interests of either their lay members or their own boards. Even the most energetic and community-aware lay members will not be able to sustain sole responsibility for communication with and for local people, let alone 'represent' them. If investment in public involvement is to grow, other methods will be needed. Nonetheless, most lay members do have experience and knowledge which may be invaluable for developing relationships with patients, carers and the wider public. To ignore or neglect this resource, where it is available, is equally mistaken. PCGs considering the transition to primary care trust status should ensure that the contribution of PCG lay members, both in advocating and enabling public involvement, is not lost in the process.

There are many other community resources for PCGs to draw on. The populations of general practices are obvious routes in to engagement with patients and carers, especially where a history of local patient participation already exists. Community health councils have played a key role in some areas, as have health authorities and local authorities, and the community and voluntary sector in London is itself an extraordinary resource. However, exploiting this resource is itself a process which requires time and investment, particularly if this means engaging with people on their terms (and about their priorities).

6.3   Finding the appropriate level of public involvement

Public involvement is controversial precisely because it concerns the power relationships between institutions and professionals on the one hand and the public and patients on the other. This tension defines a range of possibilities for involvement, described in various ways in the literature. [13,14] These can be summarised as the following four possibilities:

- informing, where information goes only one way, from professionals to the public
- consulting, where information goes both ways but professionals retain power over decision-making
- partnership, where power and decision-making are shared between professionals and lay people

- empowerment, where decision-making power is held by lay people.

The aims, objectives and methods identified by respondents in this study revealed intentions across all of these possibilities, but they are dominated by the first two. Although there is widespread commitment to going beyond informing patients and the public about the PCG and its services, the agenda for involvement is still usually set and controlled by the PCG.

Once again, realism is essential. PCG members must be honest about what level of public involvement they can manage and equally honest with local people and local stakeholders about what involvement they can expect. Although some will want their PCGs to move beyond consultation to more active engagement with their communities, a PCG which does high quality consultation will be building a better reputation in the community than a PCG which offers partnership with community stakeholders but fails to deliver.

6.4   Defining success in public involvement for PCGs

This discussion has explored the plurality of the 'publics' which PCGs want to involve and the different levels of their involvement. The possible outcomes of PCG public involvement initiatives are also diverse. They concern the ways PCGs operate; the appropriateness of their decisions; the nature, quality and equity of the services they deliver and the trust which they build within local communities. They also concern the knowledge, skills, health, confidence and satisfaction of their users and the capacity of local people and communities to control their health and health care.

Given the constraints that PCGs are working under, prioritisation within these outcomes has been inevitable. Some PCGs are focused on their corporate decision-making; others are interested in the quality of services; and others still want local communities to set their own health priorities.

As public involvement can mean different things to people within organisations as well as between organisations, it is crucial that PCGs are clear about what they mean by public involvement;[15] what their priorities are; and what, for them, will be the key to success. However, the design, implementation and evaluation of public involvement initiatives should also be sensitive to the connections between organisational, service delivery, user and community outcomes.

Finally, if public involvement is perceived to be an organisational value in itself, rather than a means to various ends, success in public involvement will be reflected in every aspect of how the PCG goes about its business: in the quality of its relationships, the nature of professional judgements, the form of its collaborative working, and its openness to shared decision-making.

References

1.   Department of Health. *Local voices: the views of local people in purchasing for health.* London: NHSME, 1992.

2.   Department of Health. *The Patient's Charter.* London: HMSO, 1992.

3.   Department of Health. *Patient partnership: building a collaborative strategy.* Leeds: NHSE, 1996.

4.   Secretary of State for Health. *The New NHS - modern, dependable.* London: Stationery Office, 1997.

5.   Department of Health. *The New NHS - modern, dependable. Establishing Primary Care Groups.* HSC 1998/065, April 1998.

6.   Department of Health. *Developing Primary Care Groups.* HSC 1998/139, August, 1998.

7.   Sue Towns. *The developing relationships between Community Health Councils and Primary Care Groups in London.* The Greater London Association of Community Health Councils, 1999.

8.   Barnes M, McIver S. *Public participation in primary care.* Birmingham: Health Services Management Centre, University of Birmingham, 1999.

9.   Lupton C, Taylor P. Coming in from the cold. *Health Service Journal* 16 March 1995.

10.   Department of Health. *A first class service: quality in the new NHS.* London: Department of Health, 1998.

11.   Department of Health. *Patient and public involvement in the new NHS.* London: Department of Health, 1999.

12.   Wilkin D, Gillam S, Leese B, editors. *Primary Care Groups/Trusts, progress and challenges: findings from the national tracker survey.* Manchester: National Primary Care Research and Development Centre (in press).

13.   Charles C, DeMaio S. Lay participation in health care decision making: a conceptual framework. *Journal of Health Politics, Policy and Law* 1993, 18(4): 881-904.

14.   Farrell C, Gilbert H. *Health Care Partnerships.* London: Kings Fund, 1996.

15.   Entwistle V. Participation: if we want to make progress, we must speak clearly. *Health Expectations* 1999, 2:1-2.